# AIR PLANE COLORING BOOK

BLUE WAVE PRESS

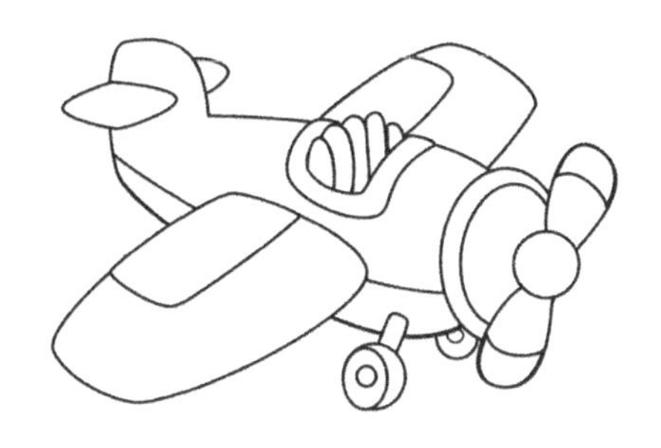

# THIS BOOK BELONGS TO:

______________________________

______________________________

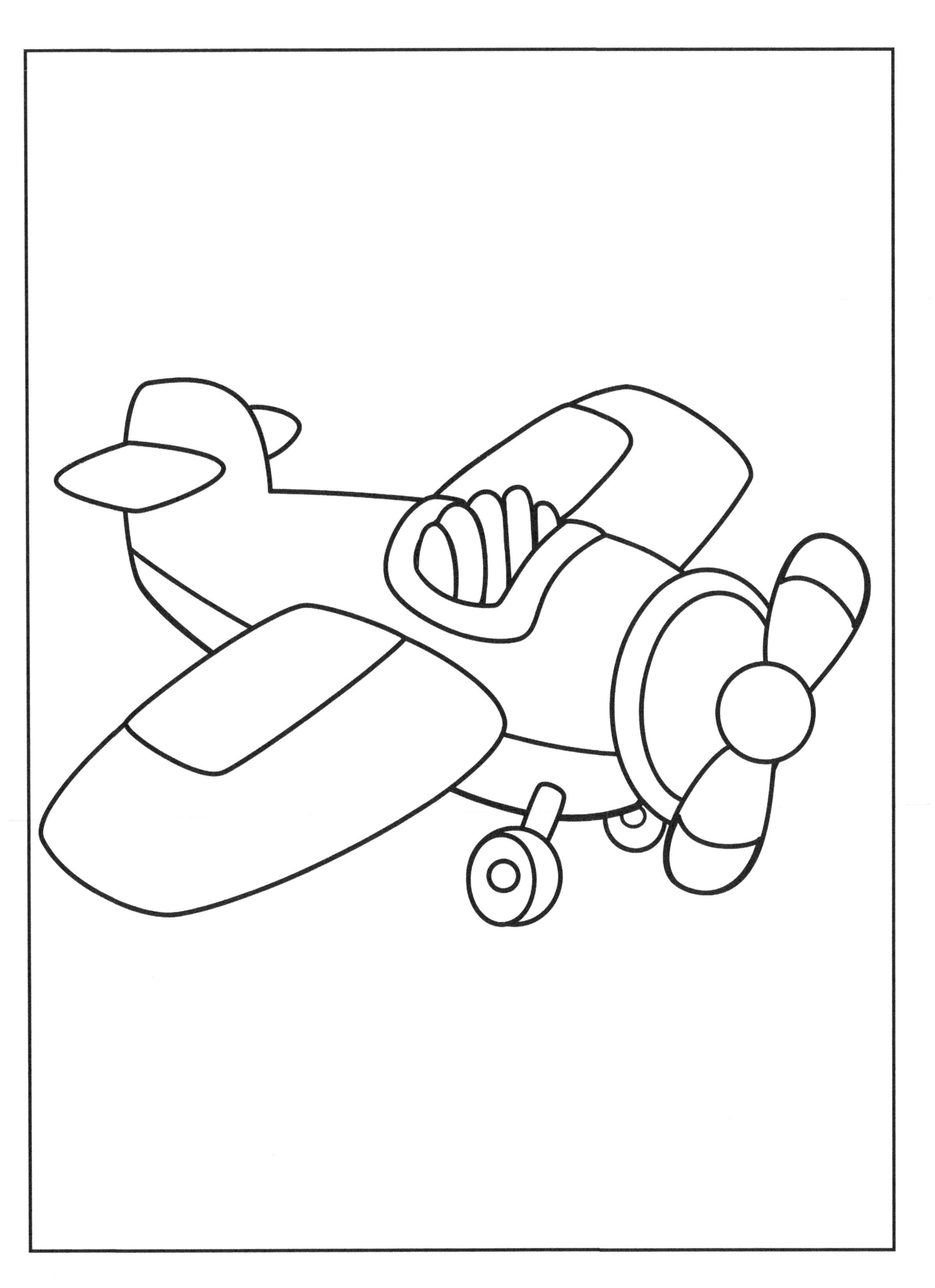

AIR
PORT

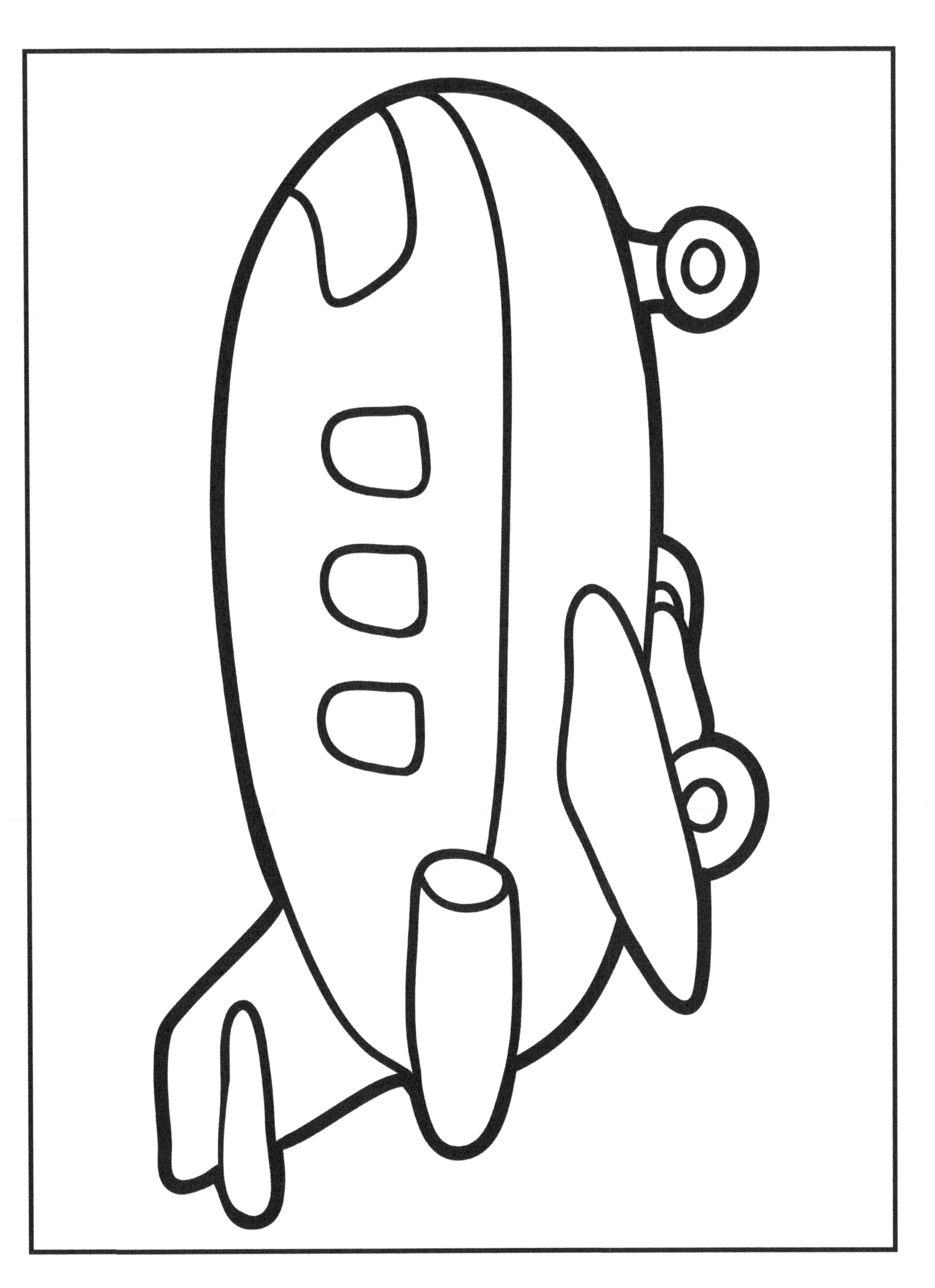

BHONARD

A B

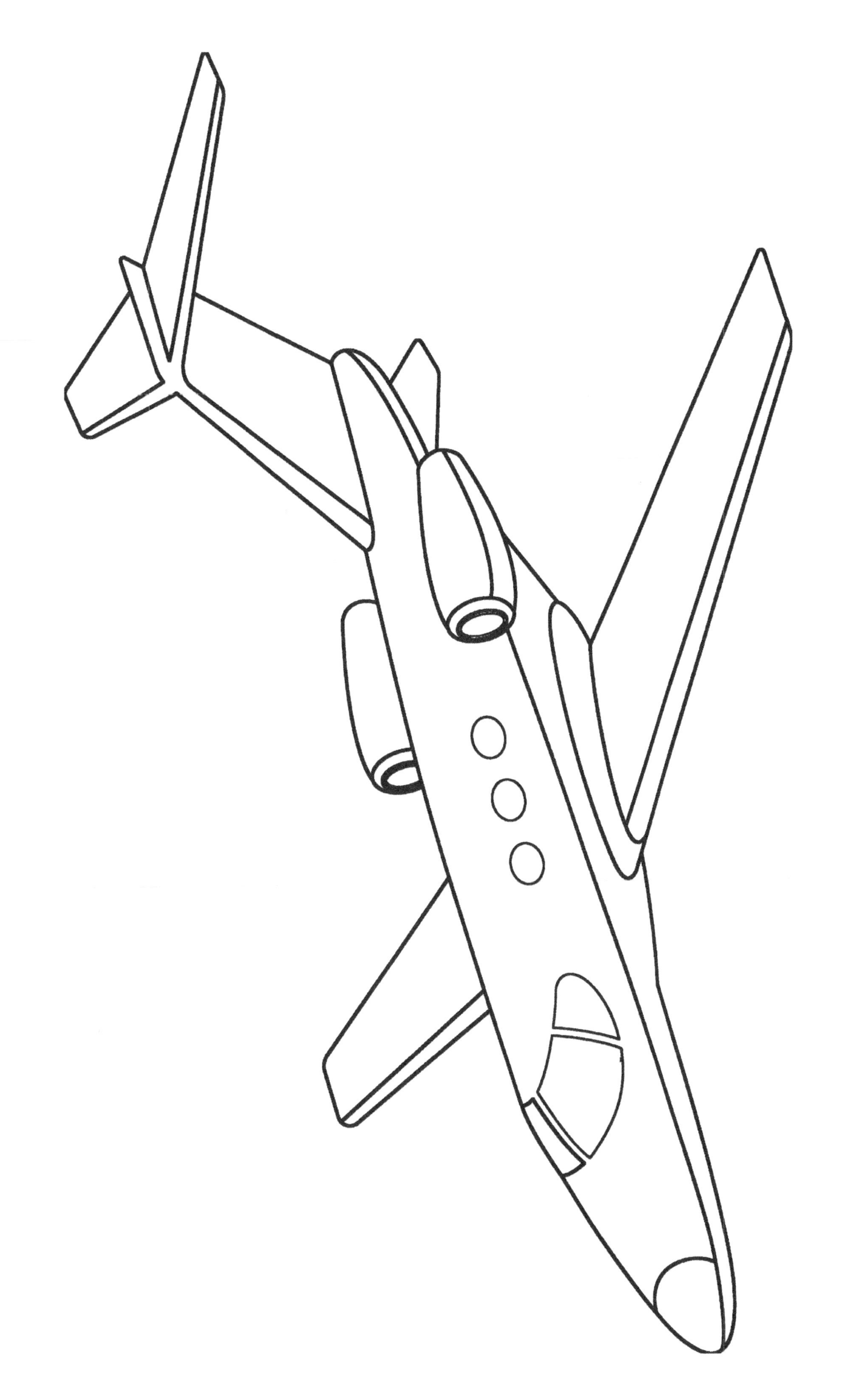

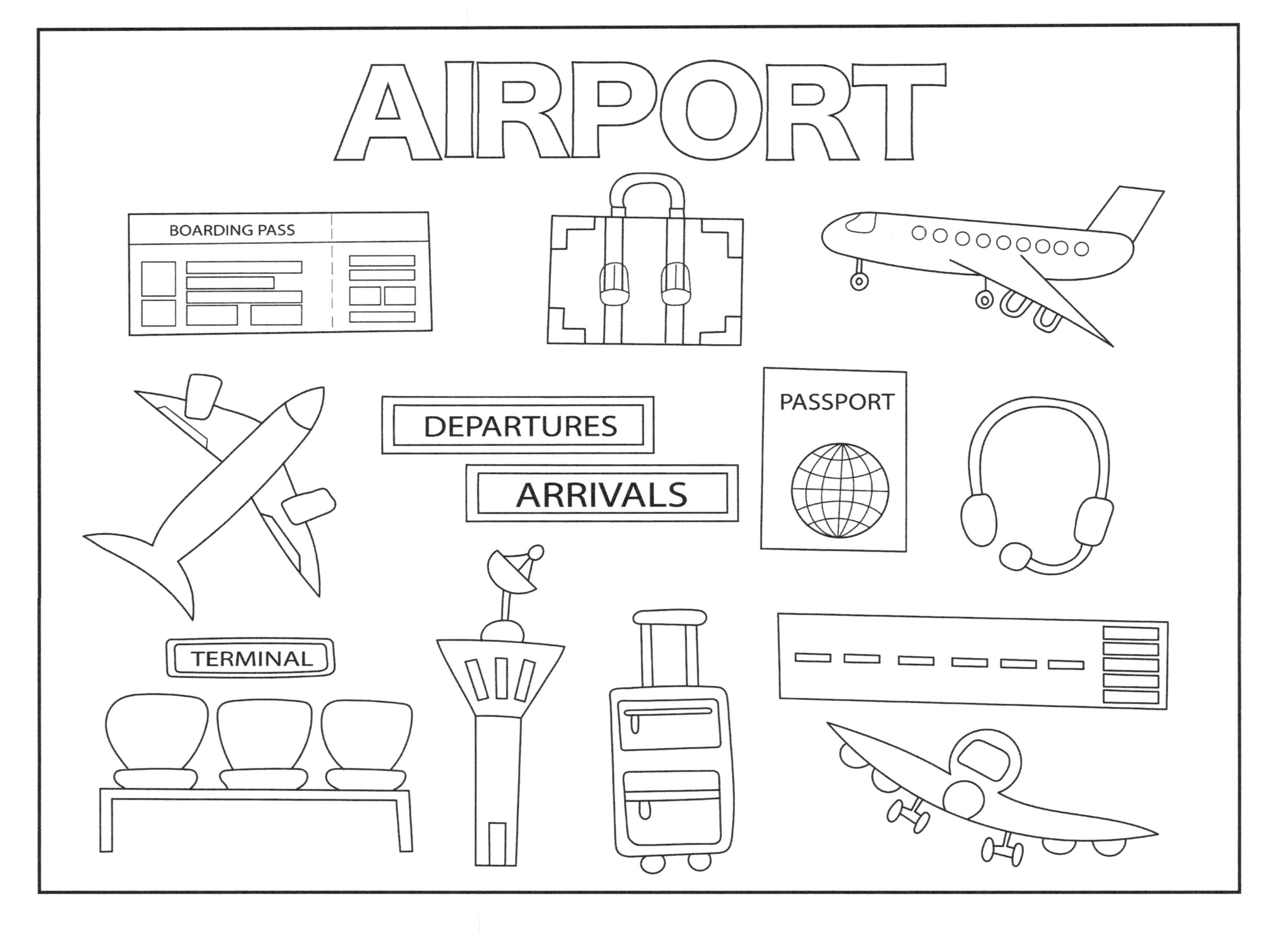
AIRPORT
BOARDING PASS
DEPARTURES
ARRIVALS
PASSPORT
TERMINAL

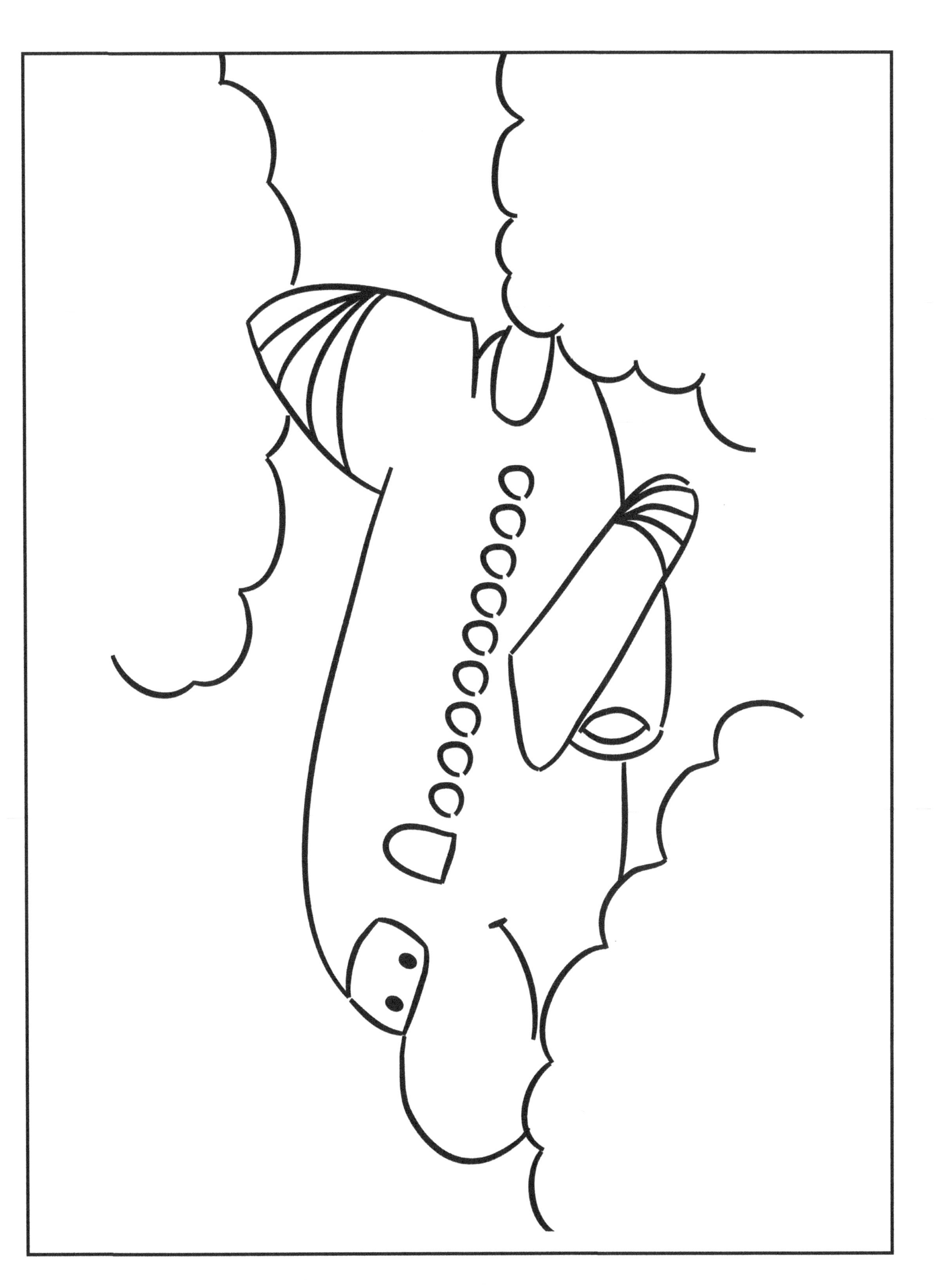

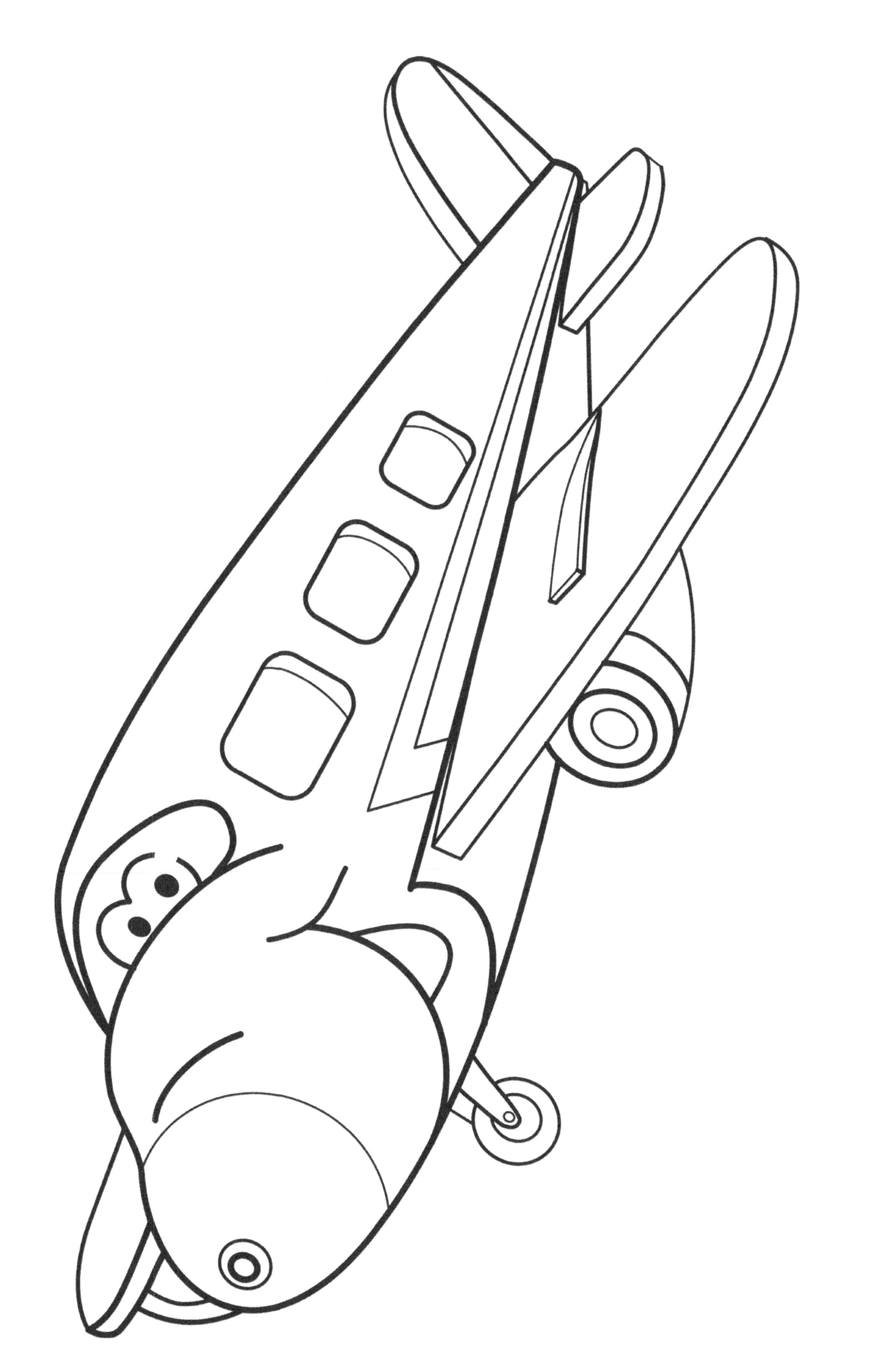

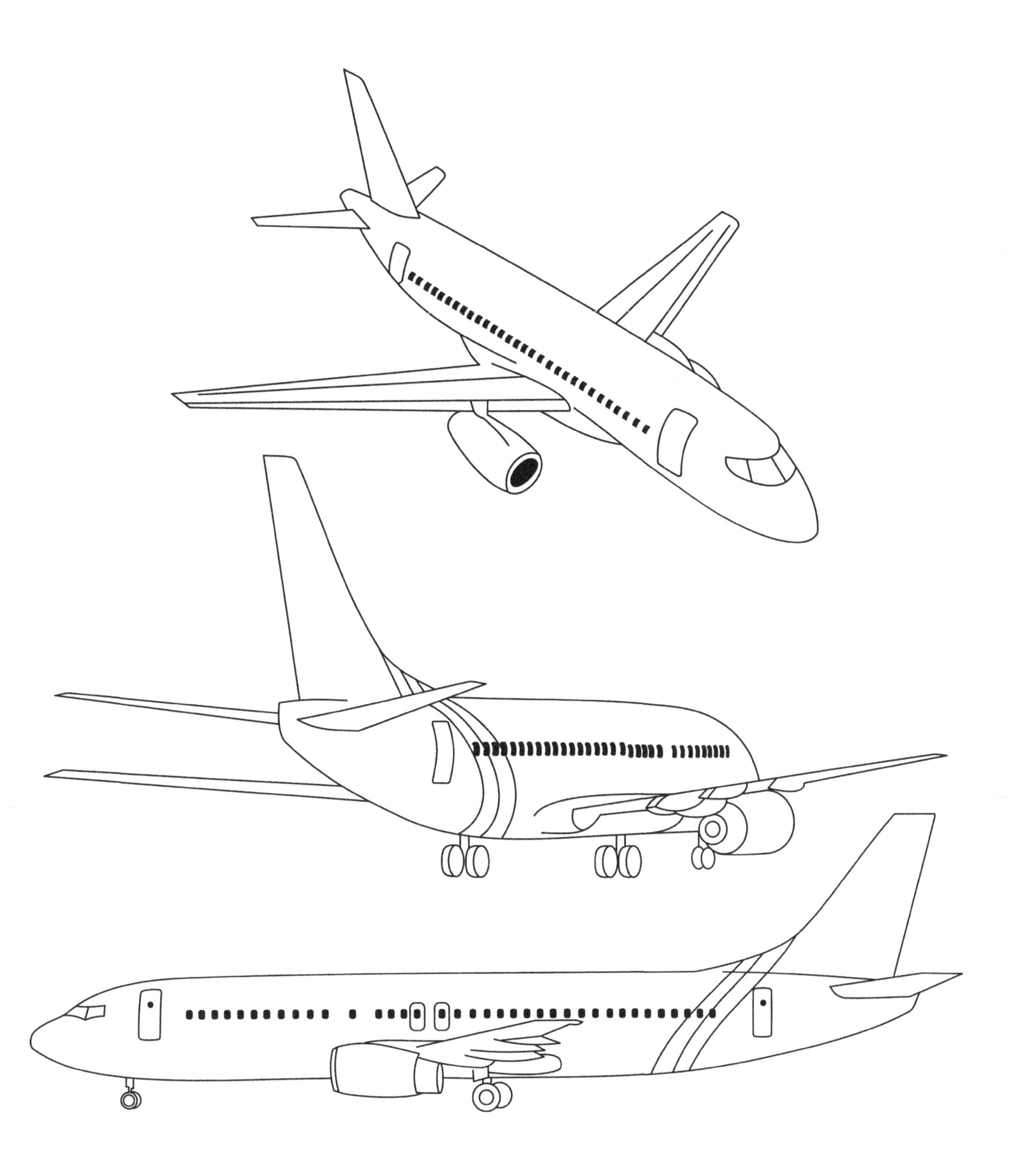

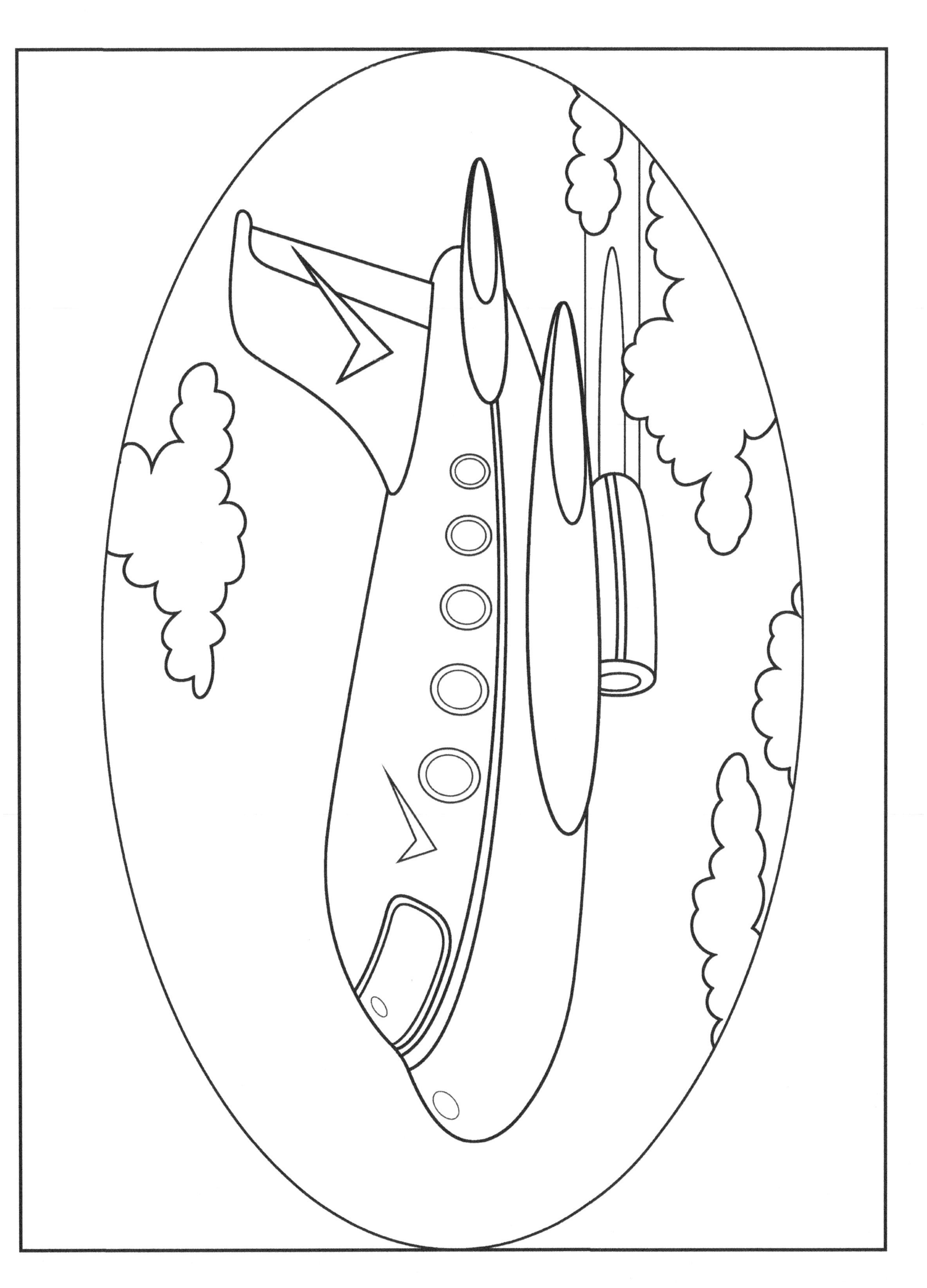

AIR PORT

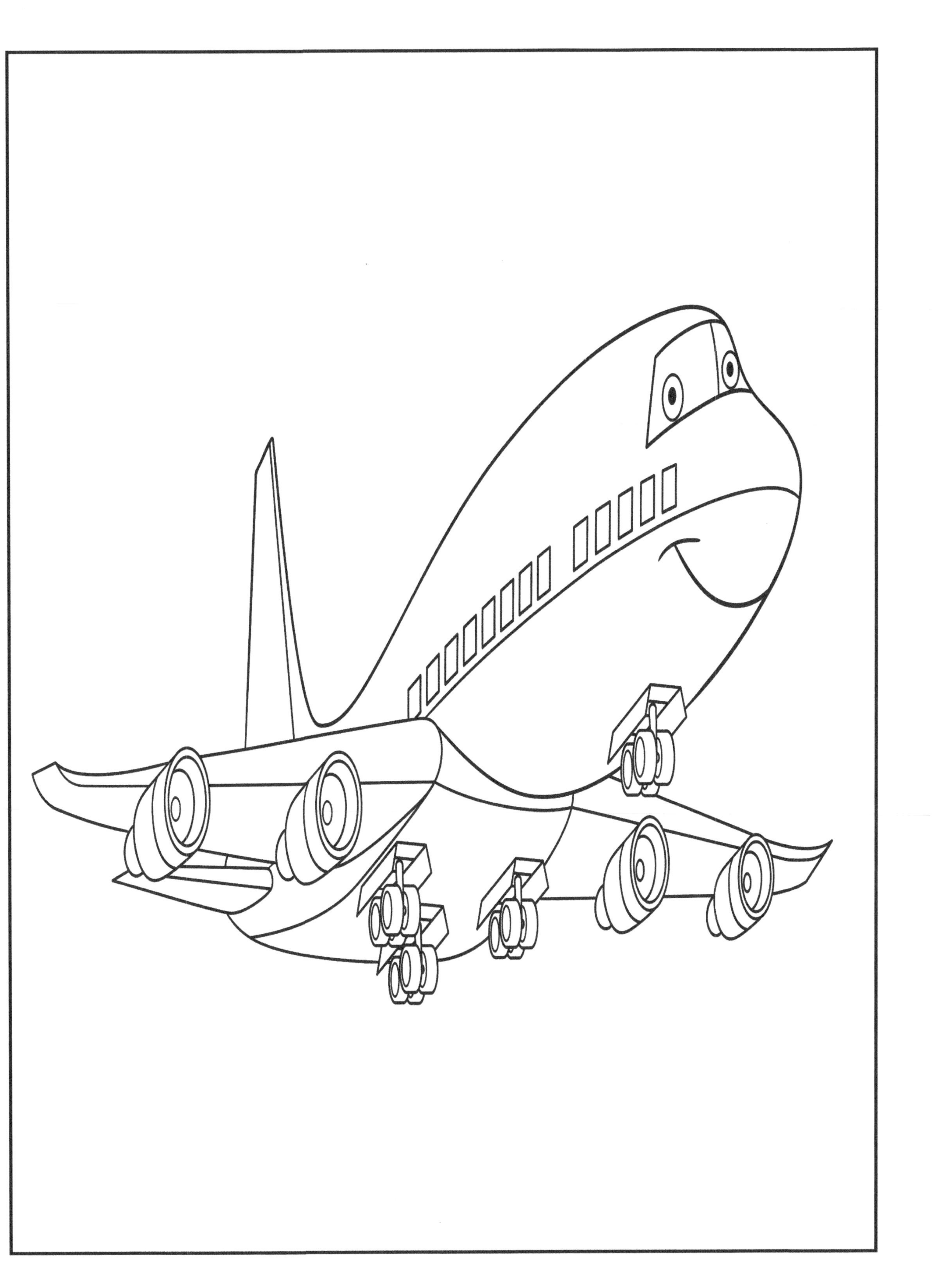

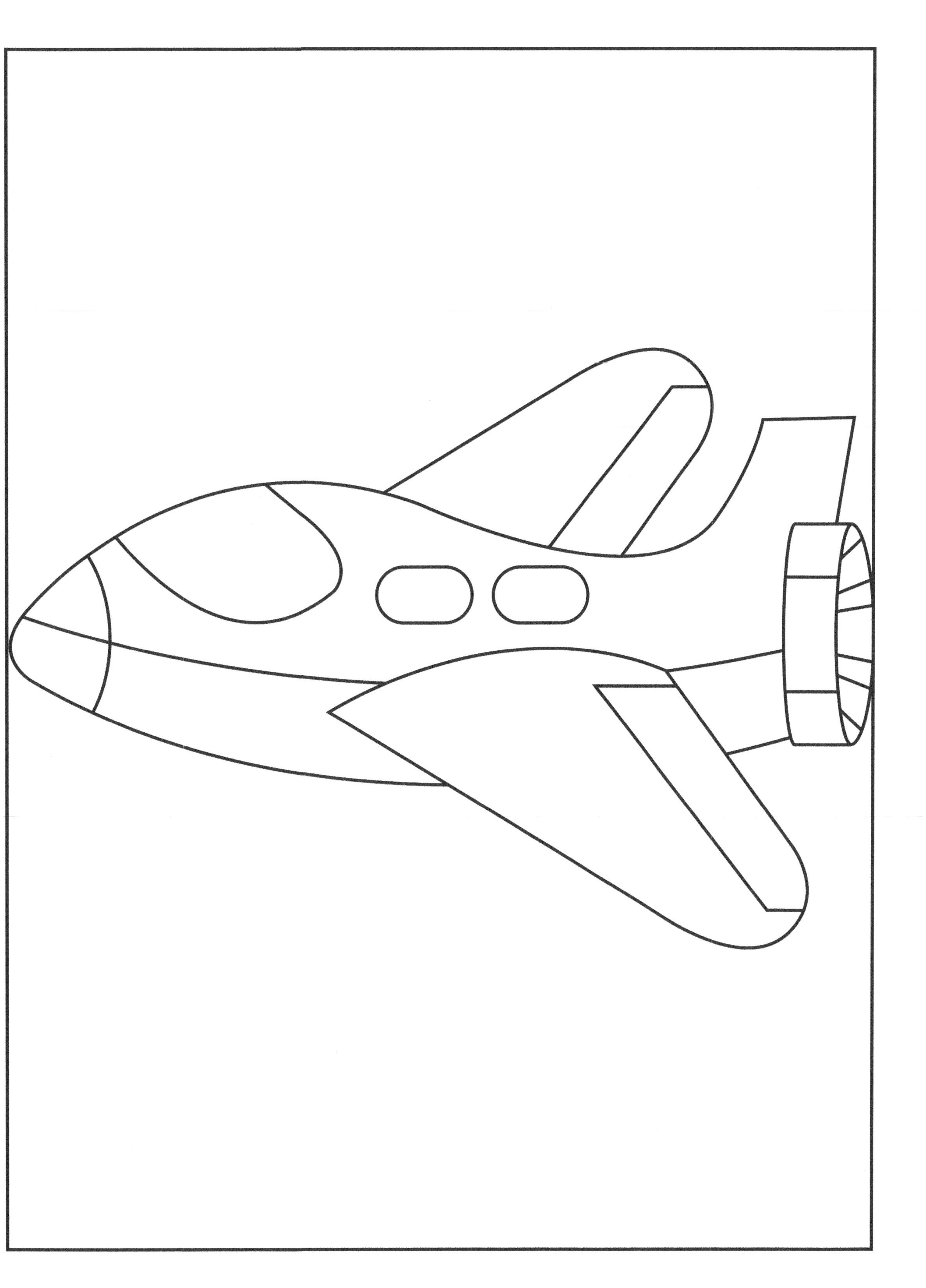

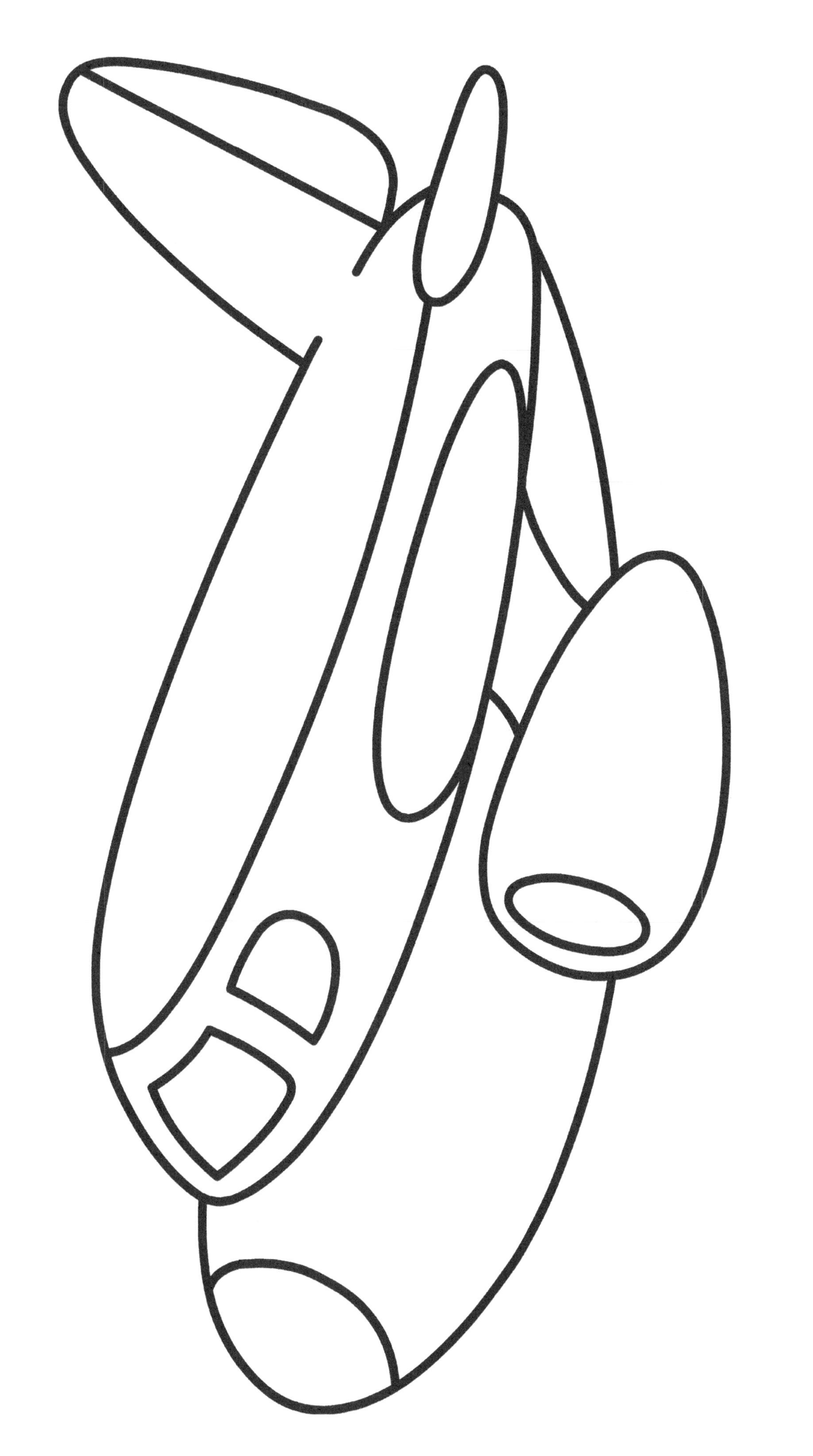

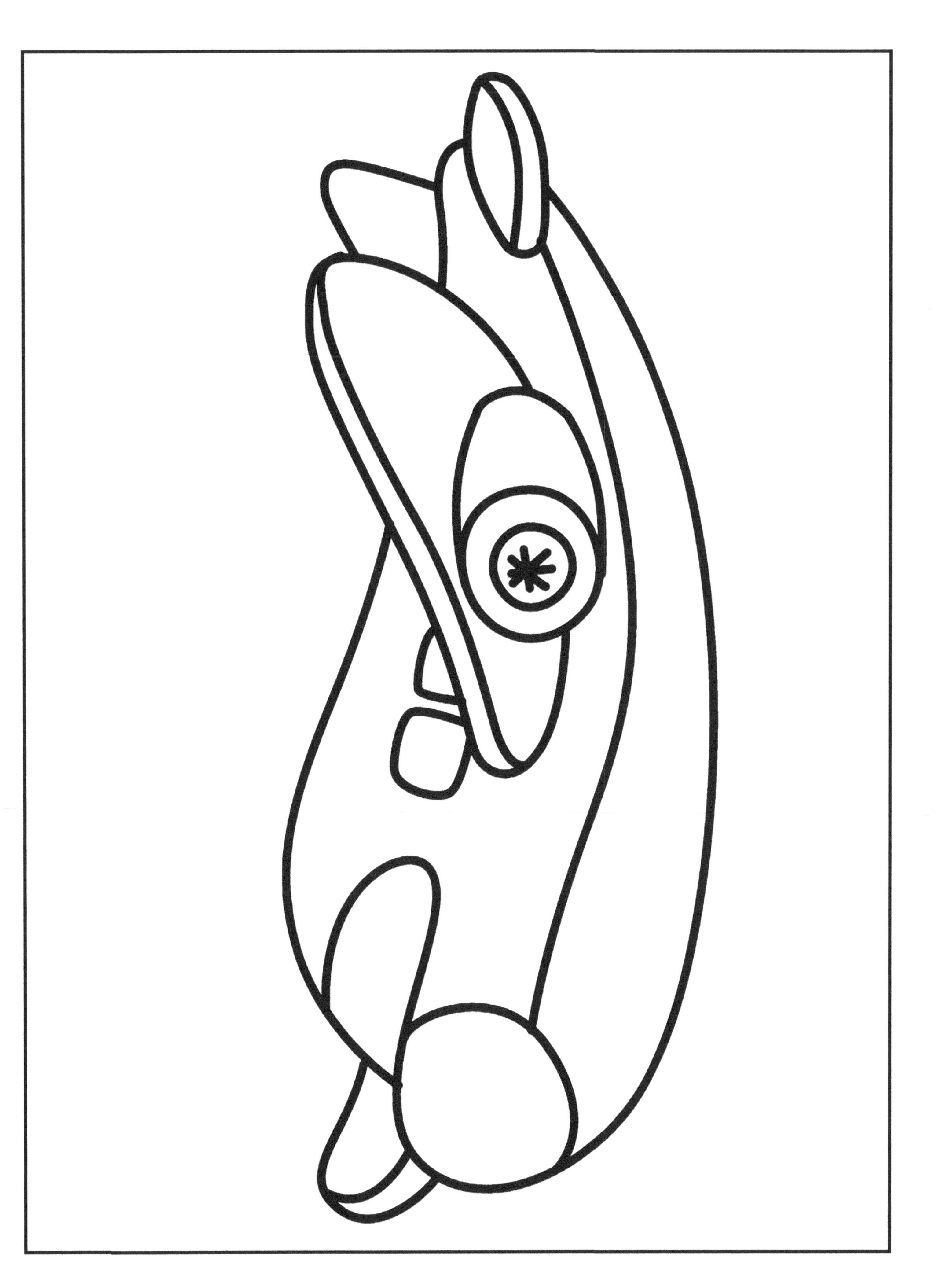

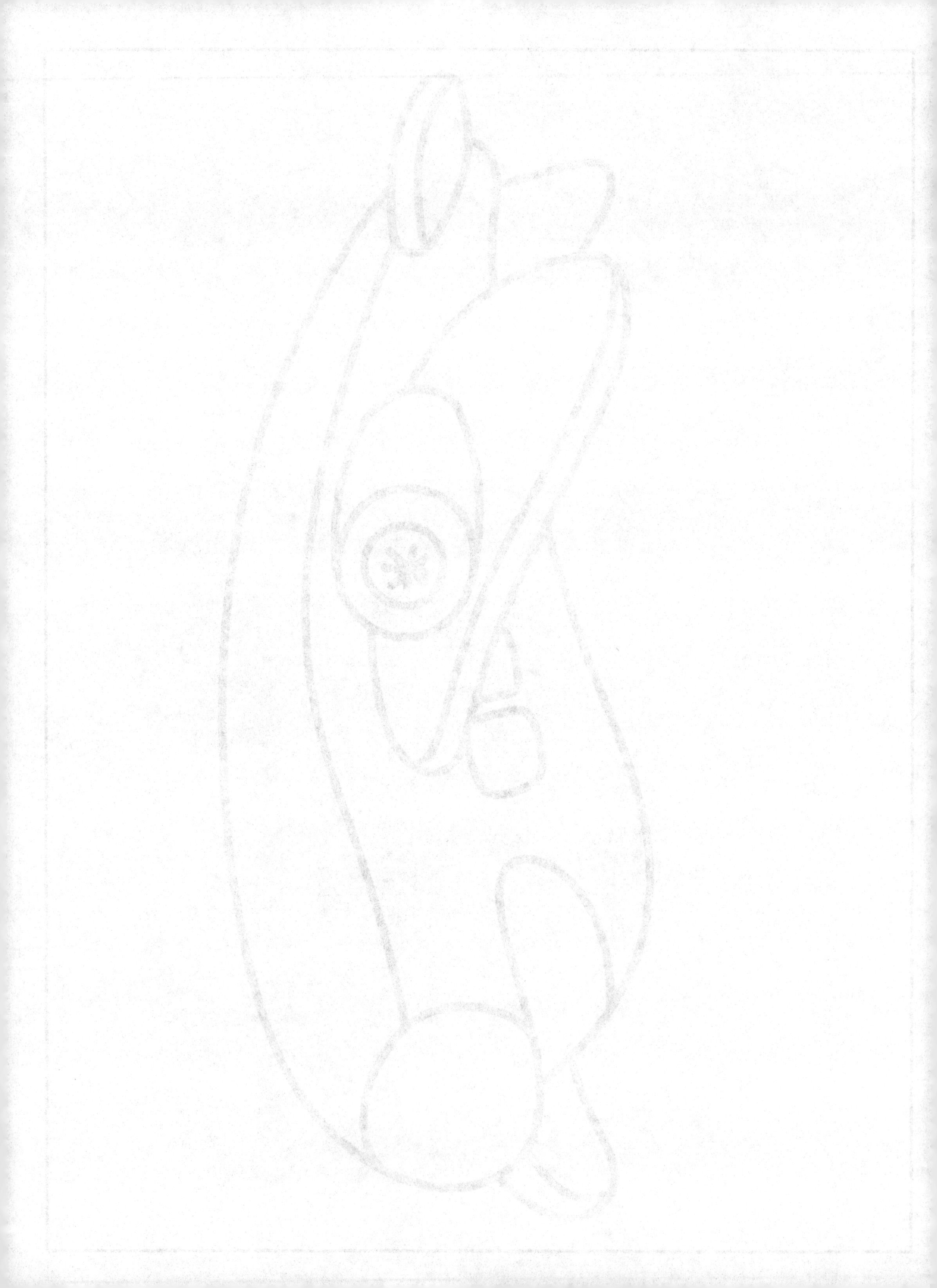

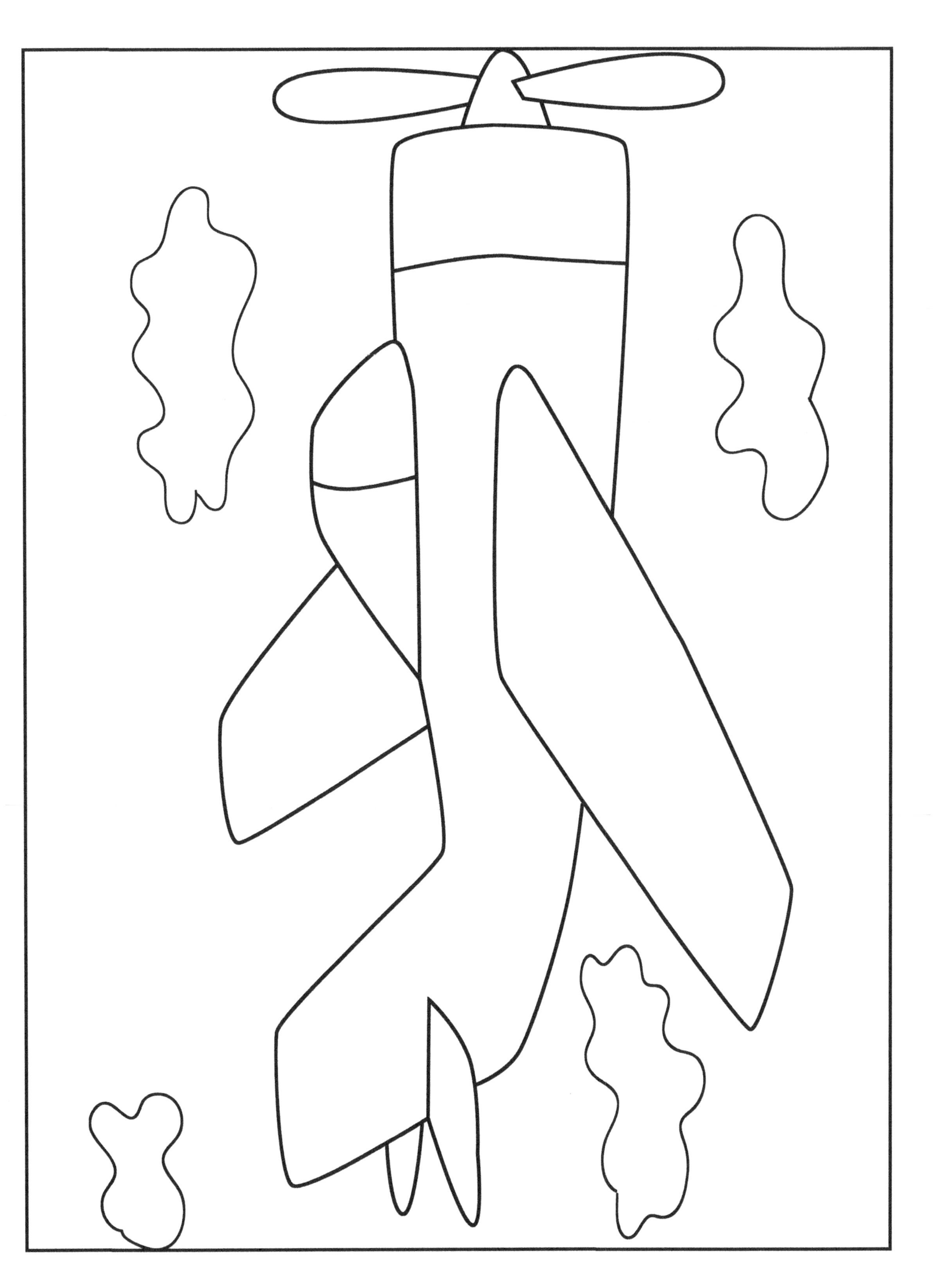

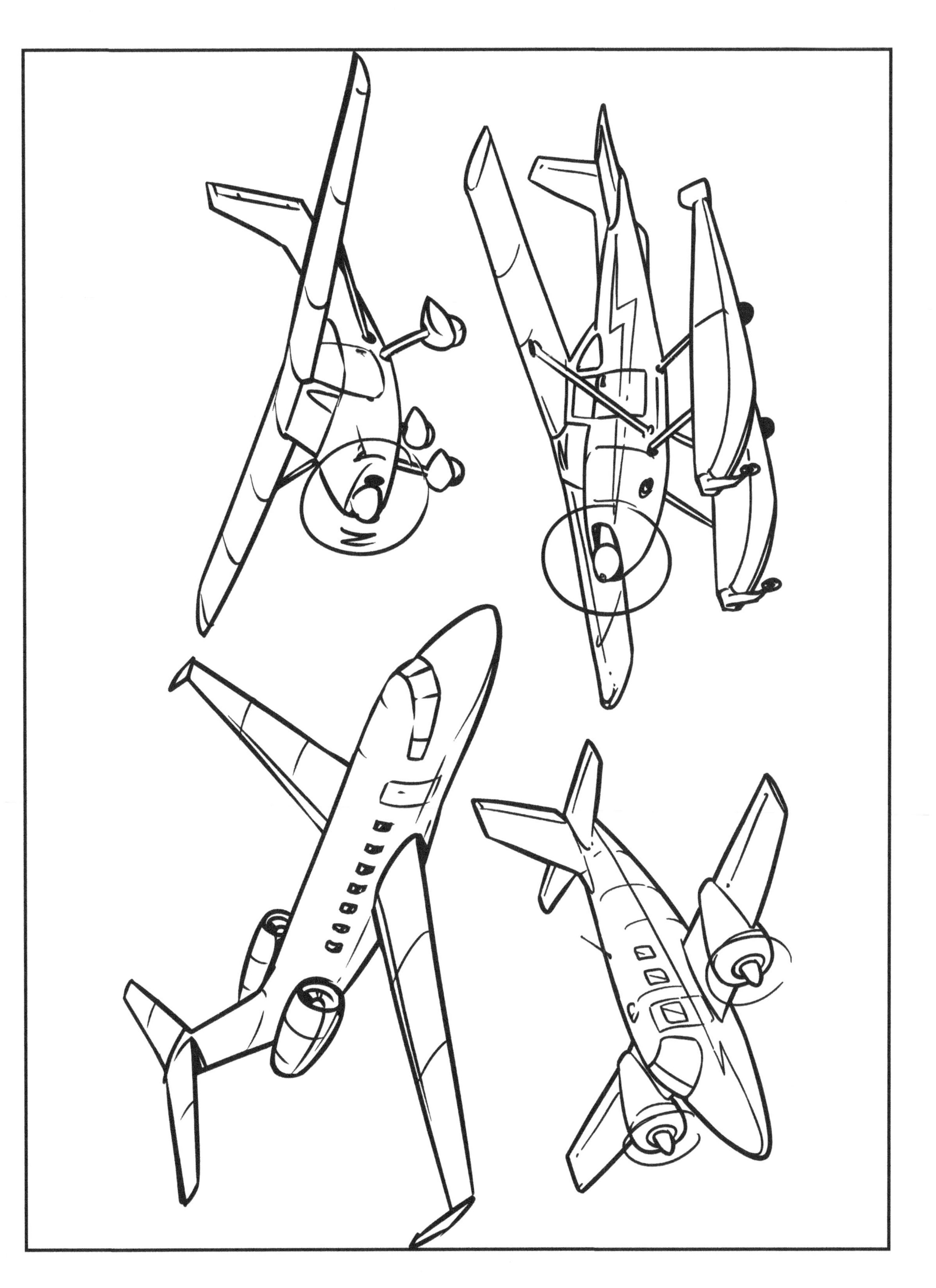

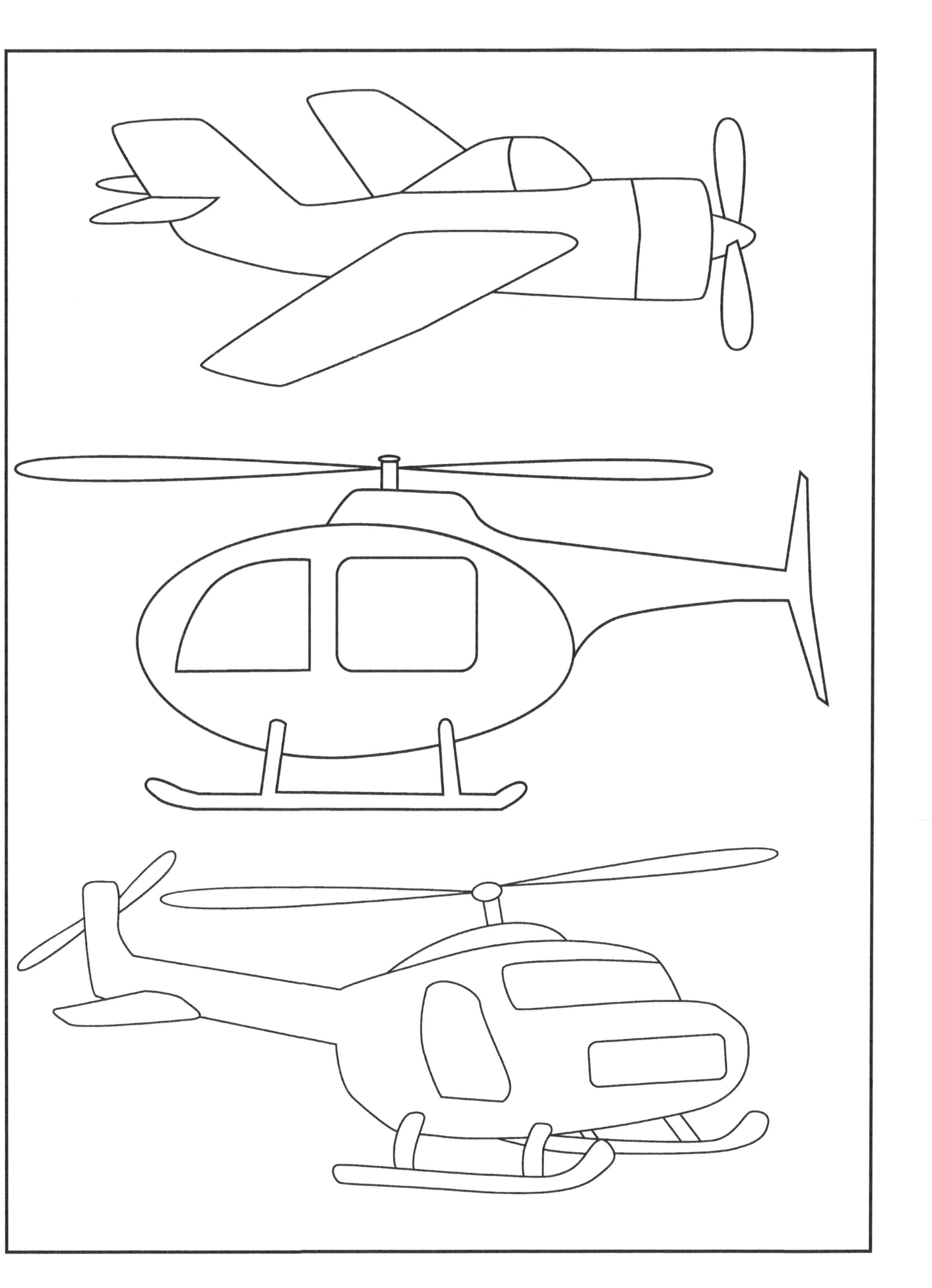

AIR PORT

# Bonus

Turn the page for bonus pages from some of our most popular coloring and activity books.

# TRUCK
## COLORING BOOK

COLORING BOOKS FOR KIDS

# Connect the Dots

## Book for Kids

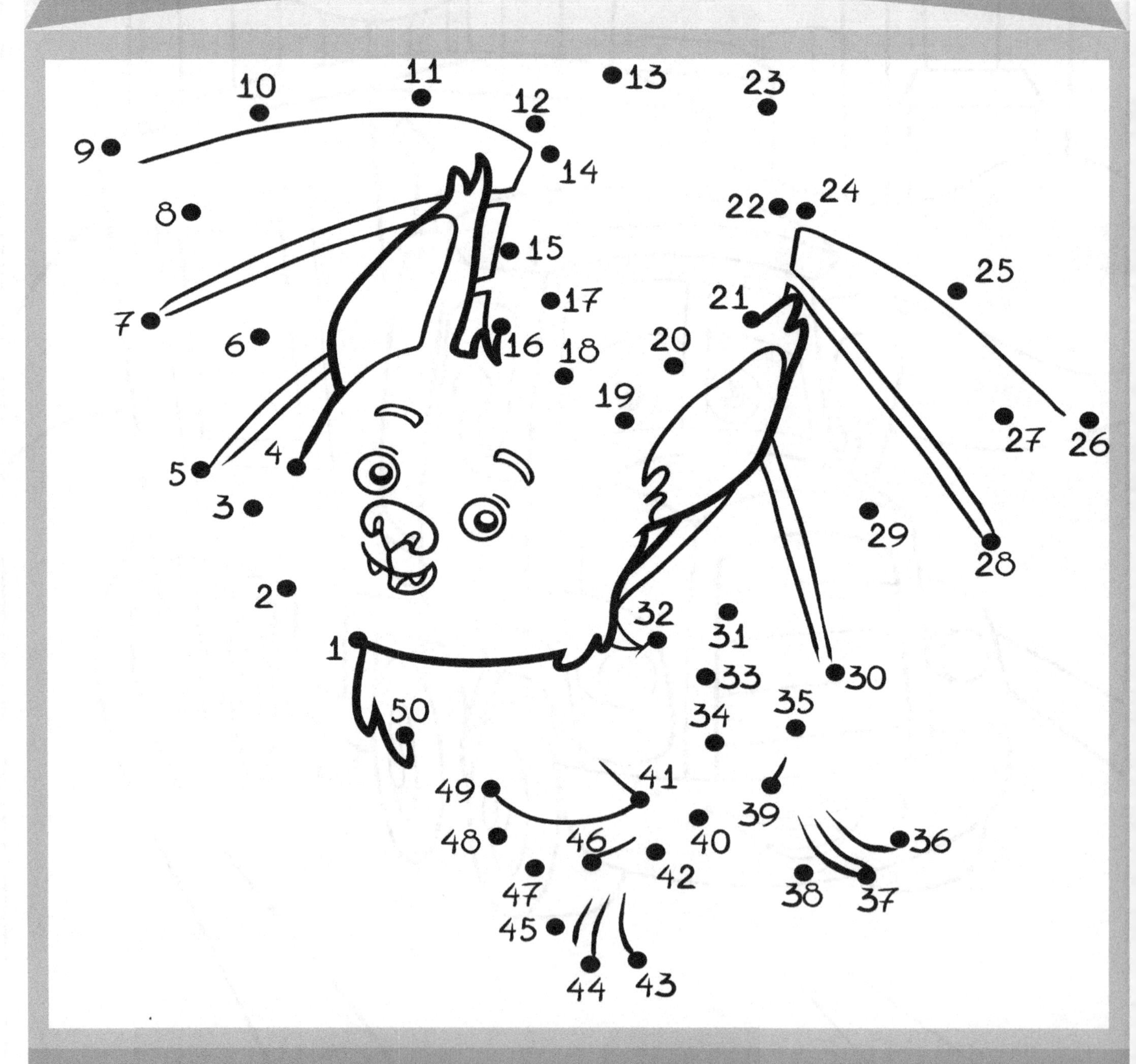

**Challenging and Fun Dot to Dot Puzzles**

# DINOSAUR

## COLORING BOOK FOR KIDS

# ROBOT COLORING BOOK

WITH BONUS ACTIVITY PAGES! MAZES, DOT TO DOT, PICTURE PUZZLES

Made in the USA
Las Vegas, NV
15 January 2024